C000003424

The Thirties

23 classic songs for keyboard

© International Music Publications Ltd
First published in 1995 by International Music Publications Ltd
International Music Publications Ltd is a Faber Music company
Bloomsbury House 74–77 Great Russell Street London WC1B 3DA
Music arranged and processed by Barnes Music Engraving Ltd
Cover image Alamy Images
Printed in England by Caligraving Ltd
All rights reserved

ISBN10: 0-571-52727-2
EAN13: 978-0-571-52727-4

All Of Me

Words and Music by Seymour Simons and Gerald Marks

Suggested Registration: Jazz Guitar
Rhythm: Swing
Tempo: ♩ = 132

All of me, _____ why not take all of me? _____

Can't you see _____ I'm no good with - out you? _____

Take my lips, _____ I want to lose them, _____

take my arms _____ I'll ne - ver use them.

Your good - bye _____ left me with eyes that cry. _____

How can I _____ go on dear with - out you? _____

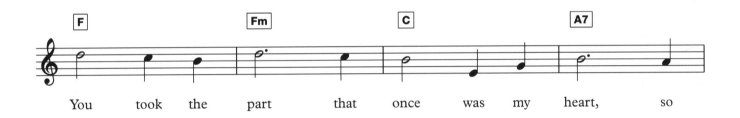

You took the part that once was my heart, so

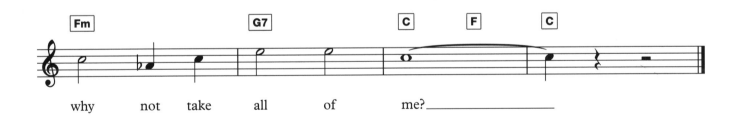

why not take all of me? _____

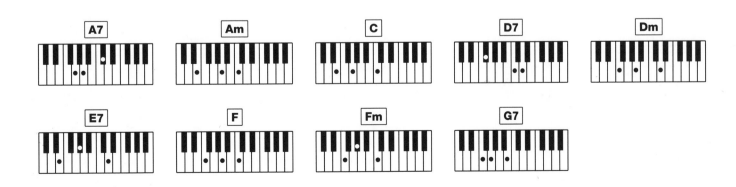

Body And Soul

Words by Robert Sour, Edward Heyman and Frank Eyton / Music by Johnny Green

Suggested Registration: Vibraphone
Rhythm: Slow Swing
Tempo: ♩ = 80

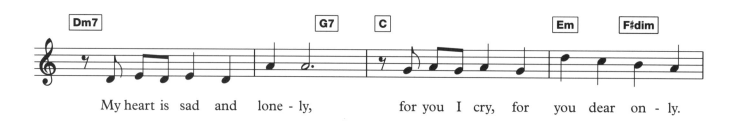

My heart is sad and lone - ly, for you I cry, for you dear on - ly.

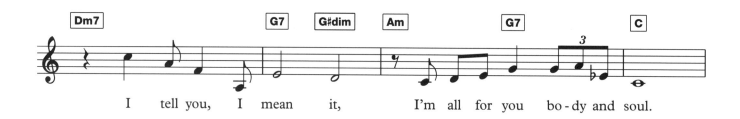

I tell you, I mean it, I'm all for you bo - dy and soul.

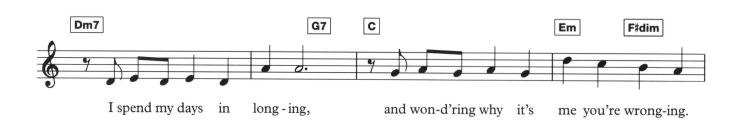

I spend my days in long - ing, and won-d'ring why it's me you're wrong-ing.

Why have-n't you seen it? I'm all for you bo - dy and soul.

I can't be-lieve it, it's hard to con-ceive it, that you'd turn a - way ro - mance.

Are you pre-tend-ing? Don't say it's the end-ing. I wish I could have one more

chance to prove, dear, my life a hell you're mak - ing. You know I'm yours for

just the tak-ing, I'd glad-ly sur - ren - der my-self to you bo-dy and soul.

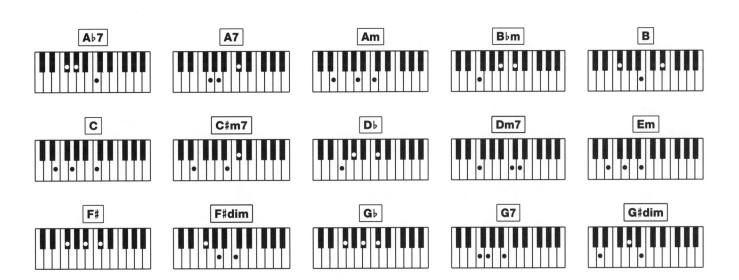

Easy To Love

Words and Music by Cole Porter

Suggested Registration: Electric Piano
Rhythm: Slow Swing
Tempo: ♩ = 104

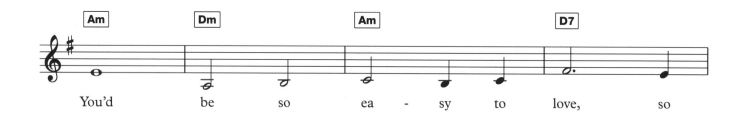

You'd be so ea - sy to love, so

ea - sy to i - do - lize all oth - ers a - bove,

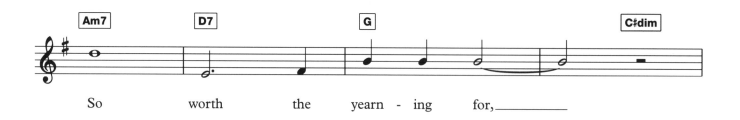

So worth the yearn - ing for, _____

so swell to keep ev - ery home - fire burn - ing for. _____

Warner Chappell Music Ltd, London W1Y 3FA

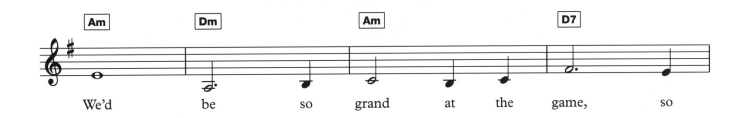

We'd be so grand at the game, so

care - free to - ge - ther, that it does seem a shame that

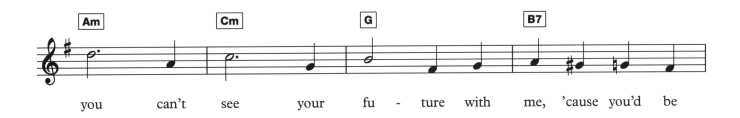

you can't see your fu - ture with me, 'cause you'd be

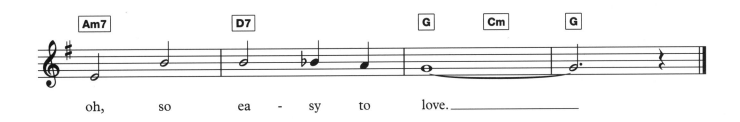

oh, so ea - sy to love. _____

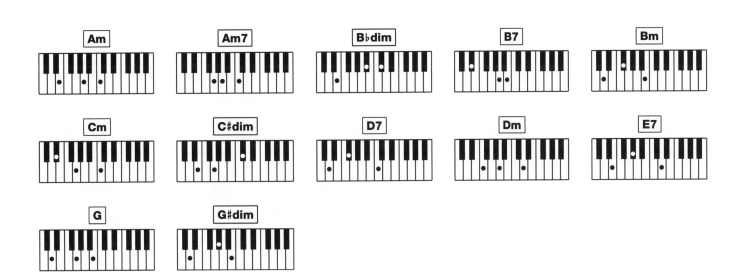

Exactly Like You

Words by Dorothy Fields / Music by Jimmy McHugh

Suggested Registration: Strings
Rhythm: Swing
Tempo: ♩ = 136

I know why I've wait - ed, know why I've been blue,

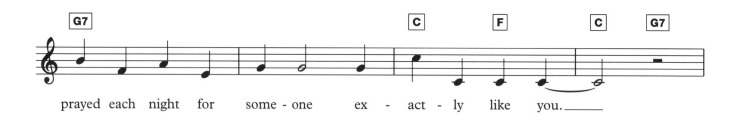

prayed each night for some - one ex - act - ly like you.____

Why should we spend mon - ey on a show or two?

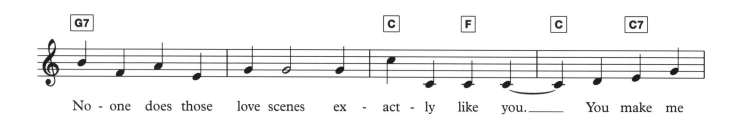

No - one does those love scenes ex - act - ly like you.____ You make me

feel so grand,_____ I want to hand the world to you._____ You seem to

un - der - stand_____ each fool-ish lit - tle scheme I'm schem-ing, dream I'm dream-ing.

Now I know why mo - ther taught me to be true,

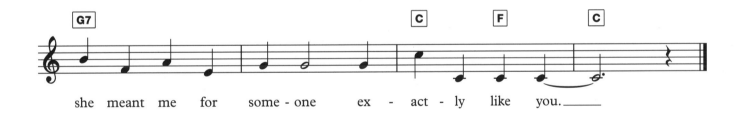

she meant me for some - one ex - act - ly like you._____

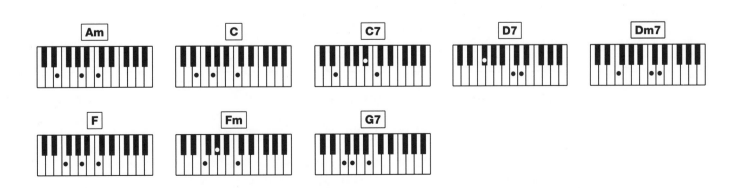

A Fine Romance

Words by Dorothy Fields / Music by Jerome Kern

Suggested Registration: Vibraphone
Rhythm: Swing
Tempo: ♩ = 132

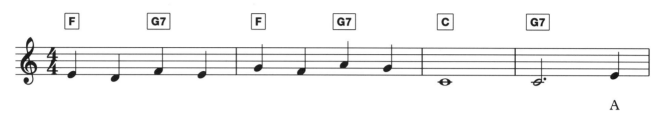

A

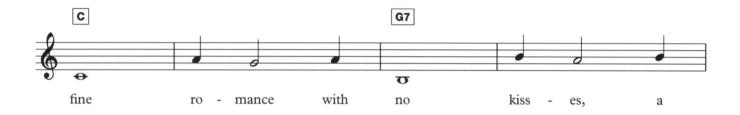

fine ro - mance with no kiss - es, a

fine ro - mance, my friend, this is. We

should be like a cou - ple of hot to - ma - toes,_____ but

you're as cold as yes - ter - day's mashed po - ta - toes._____ A

fine   ro - mance,   you   won't   nes - tle,   a

fine   ro - mance,   you   won't   wres - tle.   I

might as well play bridge with my old maid aunts,   I have - n't got a

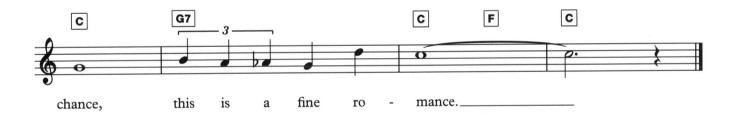

chance,   this is a fine ro - mance._____

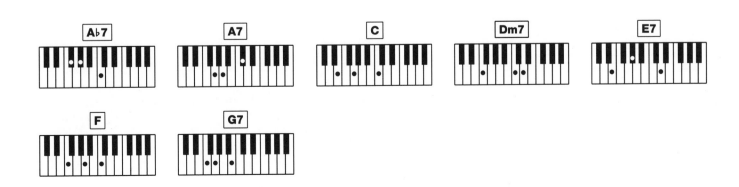

A Foggy Day

Music and Lyrics by George Gershwin and Ira Gershwin

Suggested Registration: Strings
Rhythm: Swing
Tempo: ♩ = 118

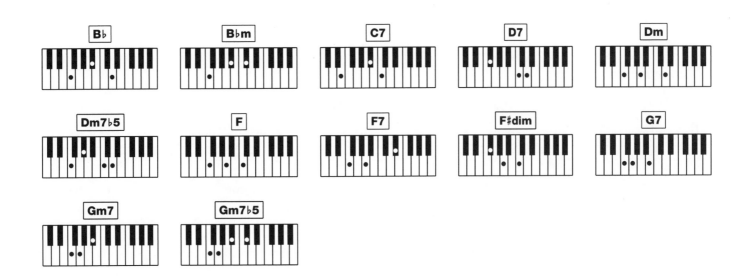

For All We Know

Words by Sam M Lewis / Music by J Fred Coots

Suggested Registration: Strings
Rhythm: Slow Swing
Tempo: ♩ = 94

For all we know, we may ne - ver meet a - gain,___

be - fore you go, make this mo - ment sweet a - gain.___

We won't say 'Good - night,' un - til the last

min - ute, I'll hold out my hand, and my heart will be

in it. For all we know, this may on - ly be a dream,_

_ we come and go like a rip - ple on a stream,_

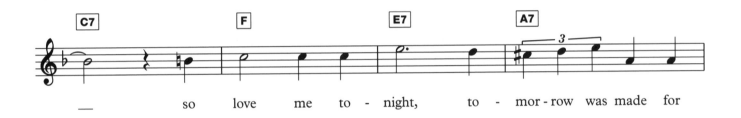

_ so love me to - night, to - mor - row was made for

some, to - mor-row may ne - ver come, for all we know._____

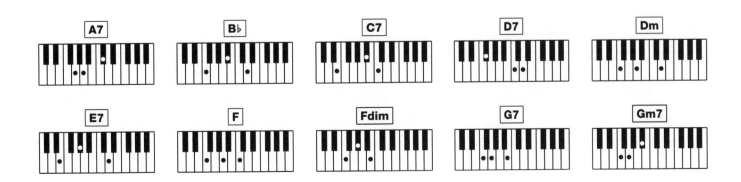

Glory Of Love

Words and Music by Billy Hill

Suggested Registration: Vibraphone
Rhythm: Swing
Tempo: ♩ = 126

You've got to

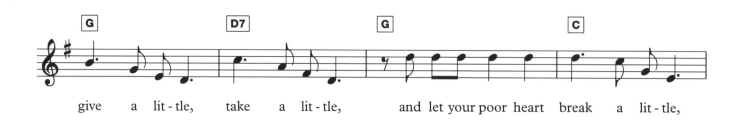

give a lit - tle, take a lit - tle, and let your poor heart break a lit - tle,

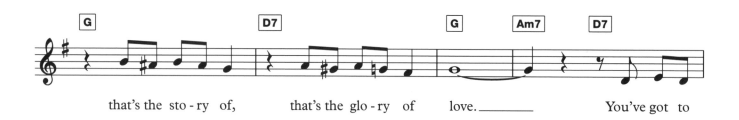

that's the sto - ry of, that's the glo - ry of love. _____ You've got to

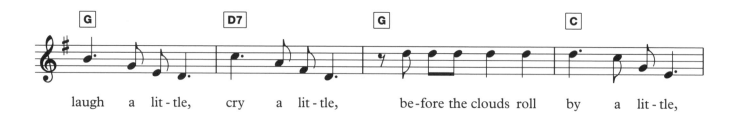

laugh a lit - tle, cry a lit - tle, be-fore the clouds roll by a lit - tle,

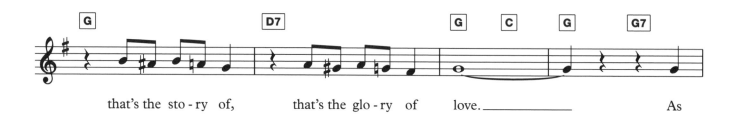

that's the sto - ry of, that's the glo - ry of love. _____ As

long   as there's   the   two of us,   we've got the world and   all   its   charms,   and

when   the world   is through with us,   we've got each oth - er's arms.   You've got to

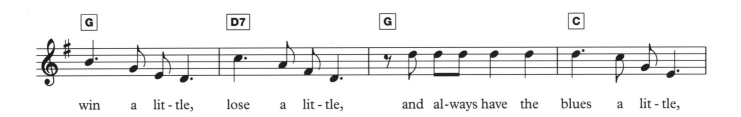

win   a lit - tle,   lose   a lit - tle,   and al-ways have the   blues   a lit - tle,

that's the sto - ry of,   that's the glo - ry of   love._____

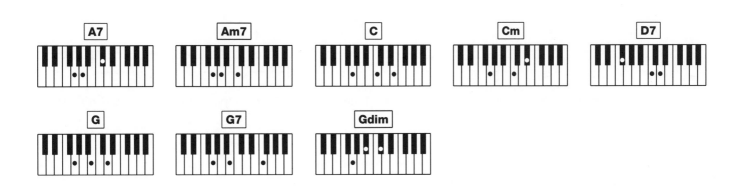

I Wanna Be Loved By You

Words by Bert Kalmar / Music by Herbert Stothart and Harry Ruby

Suggested Registration: Saxophone
Rhythm: Swing
Tempo: ♩ = 112

I wan-na be loved by you, just you, and no-bo-dy else but you,

I wan-na be loved by you a - lone,_____ poo-poo - pa-doop.

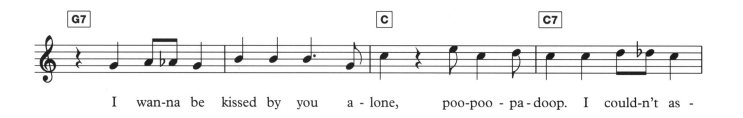

I wan-na be kissed by you, just you, and no-bo-dy else but you,

I wan-na be kissed by you a - lone, poo-poo - pa-doop. I could-n't as -

-pire_____ to a - ny-thing high - er,_____ than fill a de -

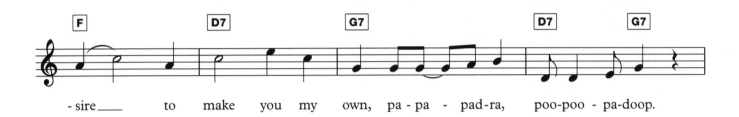

- sire___ to make you my own, pa - pa - pad-ra, poo-poo - pa-doop.

I wan-na be loved by you, just you, and no-bo-dy else but you,

I wan-na be loved by you a - lone, pa-dap-pa dap-pa-dab, po-poo - pa-doop.

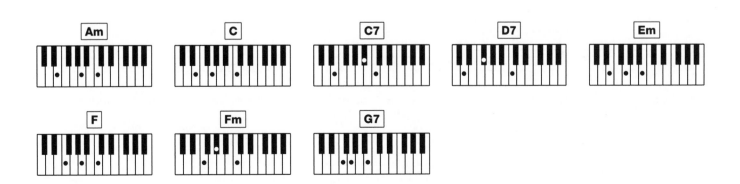

I'VE GOT YOU UNDER MY SKIN

Words and Music by Cole Porter

Suggested Registration: Vibraphone
Rhythm: Swing
Tempo: ♩ = 106

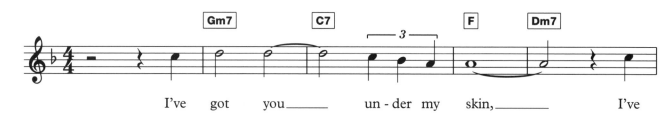

I've got you_____ un-der my skin,_____ I've

got you_____ deep in the heart of me,_____ so

deep in my heart_____ you're real-ly a part of me,_____ I've

got you_____ un-der my skin._____ I'll

sac-ri-fice a-ny-thing, come what might, for the sake of hav-ing you

near, in spite of the warn-ing voice that comes in the night, and re-

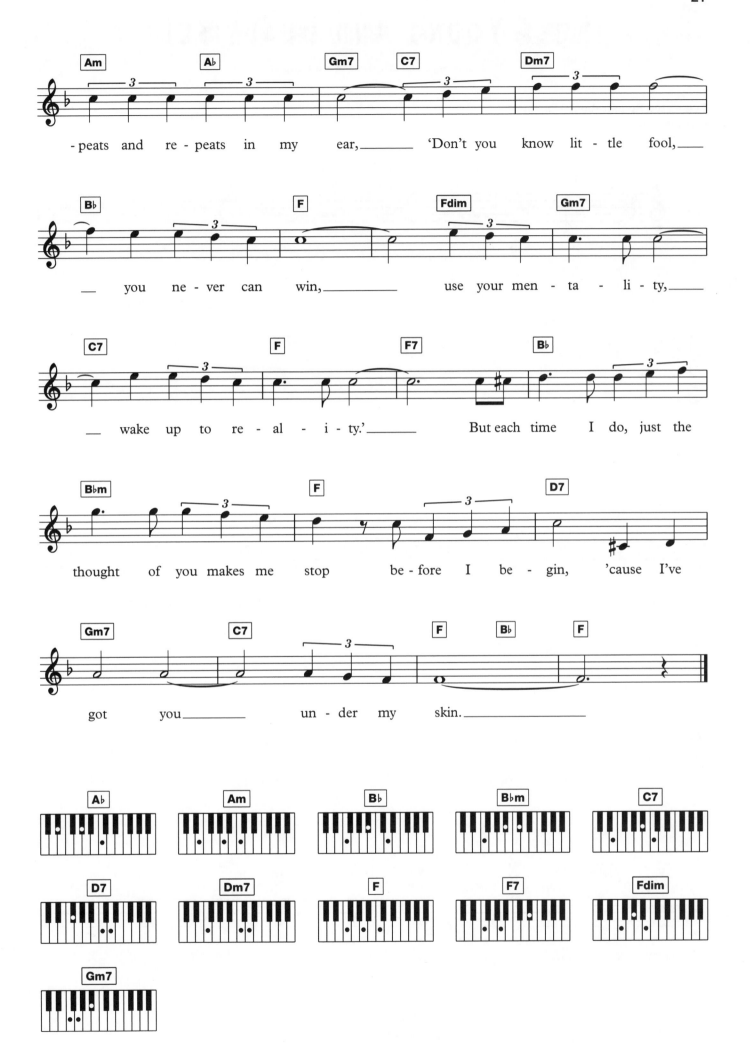

Keep Young And Beautiful

Words by Al Dubin / Music by Harry Warren

Suggested Registration: Vibraphone
Rhythm: Swing
Tempo: ♩ = 130

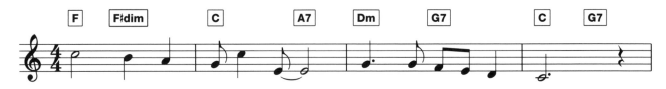

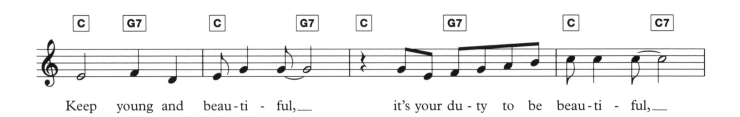

Keep young and beau-ti - ful,___ it's your du - ty to be beau-ti - ful,___

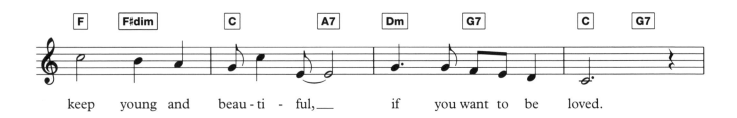

keep young and beau-ti - ful,___ if you want to be loved.

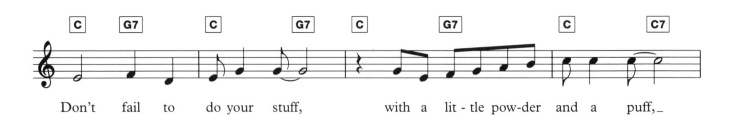

Don't fail to do your stuff, with a lit - tle pow-der and a puff,_

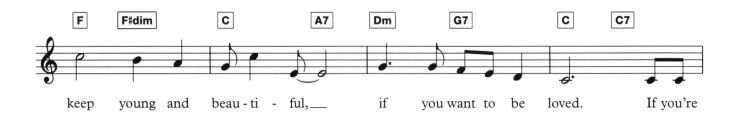

keep young and beau-ti - ful,___ if you want to be loved. If you're

wise, ex - er - cise all the fat off, take it off, off - a here, off - a there. When you're

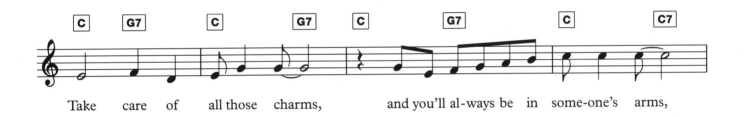

seen a - ny-where with your hat off, have a Mar - cel wave in your hair.

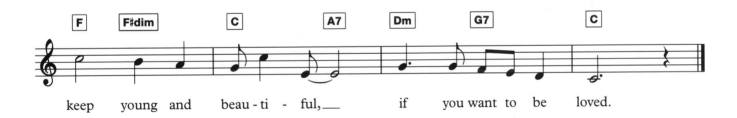

Take care of all those charms, and you'll al-ways be in some-one's arms,

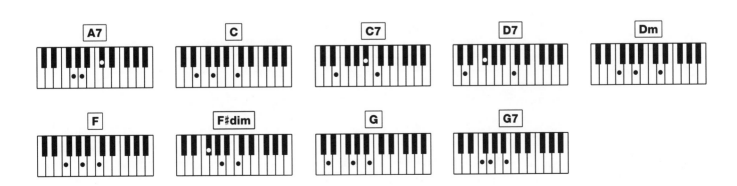

keep young and beau - ti - ful,___ if you want to be loved.

The Lady Is A Tramp

Words by Lorenz Hart / Music by Richard Rodgers

Suggested Registration: Saxophone
Rhythm: Swing
Tempo: ♩ = 132

I get too hun-gry for din-ner at eight,___

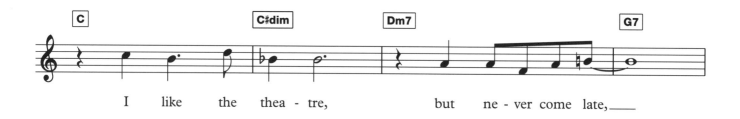

I like the thea-tre, but ne-ver come late,___

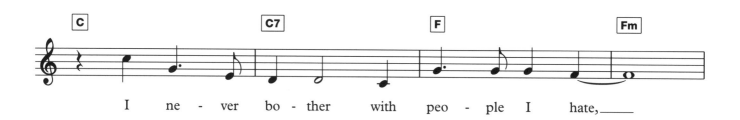

I ne-ver bo-ther with peo-ple I hate,___

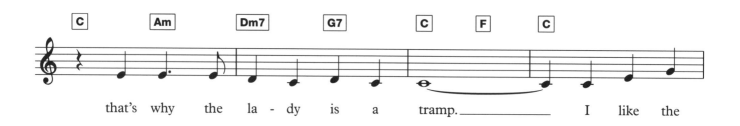

that's why the la-dy is a tramp._____ I like the

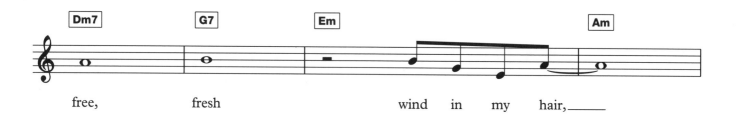

free, fresh wind in my hair,___

life with-out care,___ I'm broke, it's oke,

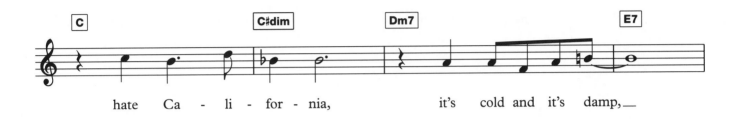

hate Ca - li - for - nia, it's cold and it's damp,___

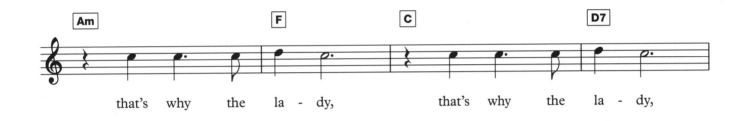

that's why the la - dy, that's why the la - dy,

that's why the la - dy is a tramp._____

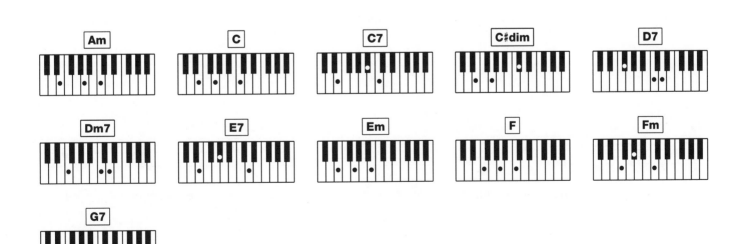

Lazy Bones

Words and Music by Johnny Mercer and Hoagy Carmichael
Additional Lyrics by Horatio Nicholls

Suggested Registration: Vibraphone
Rhythm: Slow Swing   *midnight*
Tempo: ♩ = 72

La - zy bones, sleep-in' in the sun, how you 'spec' to get your

day's work done? Ne - ver get your day's work done,

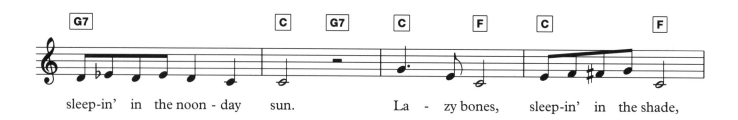

sleep-in' in the noon - day sun. La - zy bones, sleep-in' in the shade,

how you 'spec' to get your corn - meal made? Ne - ver get your corn - meal made,

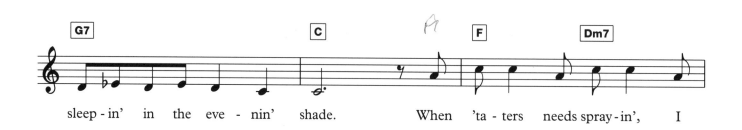

sleep - in' in the eve - nin' shade. When 'ta - ters needs spray-in', I

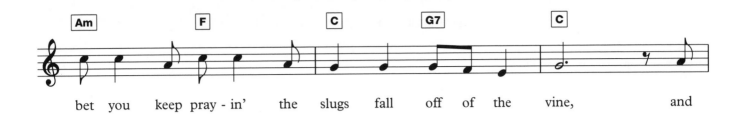

bet you keep pray - in' the slugs fall off of the vine, and

when you go fish-in', I bet you keep wish-in' the fish won't grab at your line.

La - zy bones, loaf-in' through the day, how you 'spec' to make a dime that way?

Ne - ver make a dime that way, he ne - ver heard a word I say!

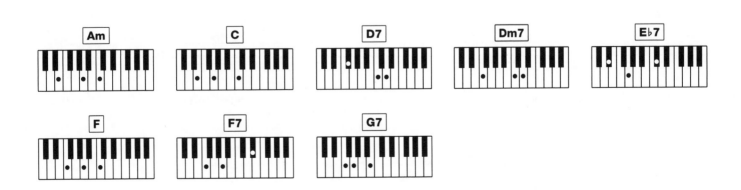

Moonlight Serenade

Words by Mitchell Parish / Music by Glenn Miller

Suggested Registration: Saxophone
Rhythm: Slow Swing
Tempo: ♩ = 72

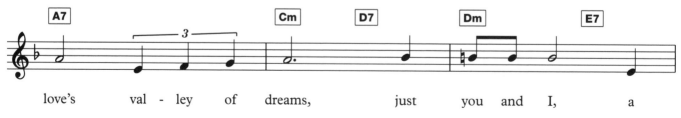

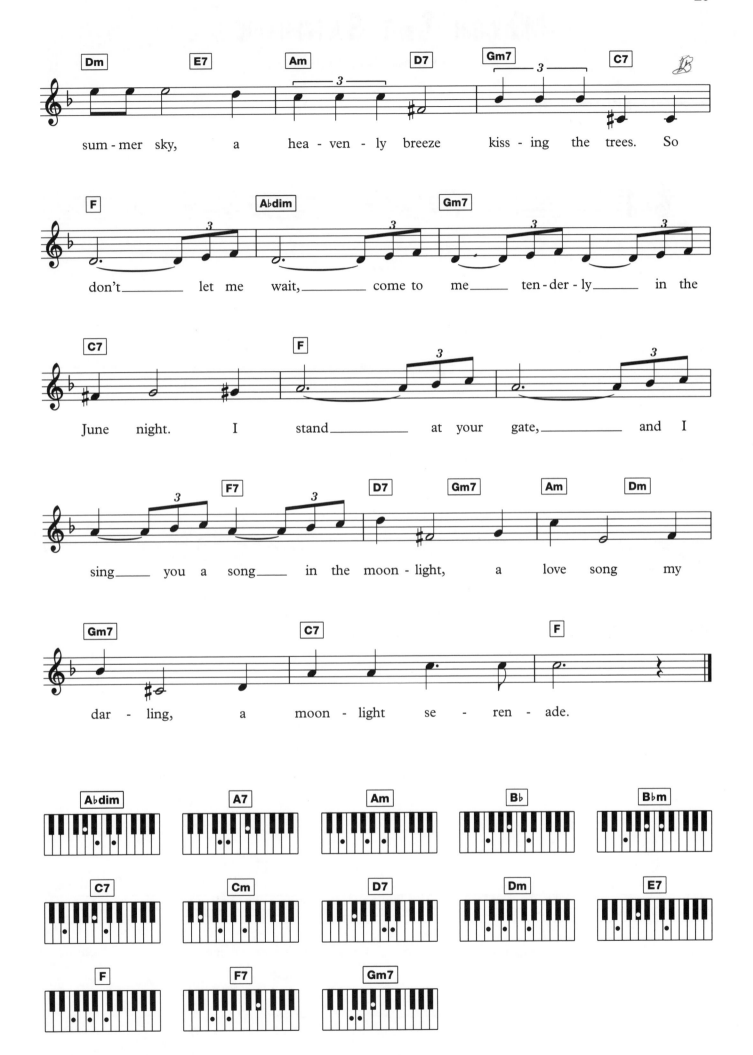

OVER THE RAINBOW

Words by EY Harburg / Music by Harold Arlen

Suggested Registration: Flute
Rhythm: Soft Rock
Tempo: ♩ = 82

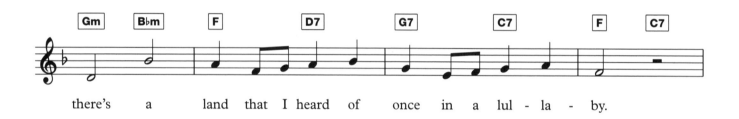

Some - where   o - ver the rain - bow,   way   up   high,

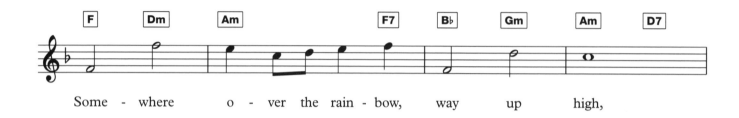

there's   a   land that I heard   of   once in a lul - la - by.

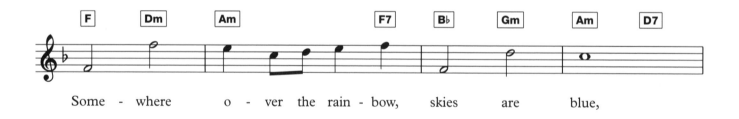

Some - where   o - ver the rain - bow,   skies   are   blue,

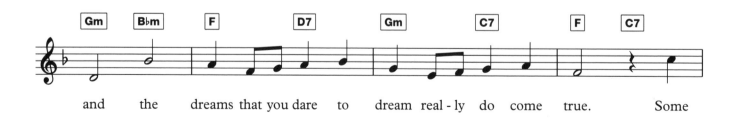

and   the   dreams that you dare   to   dream real - ly do come   true.   Some

day I'll wish up-on a star, and wake up where the clouds are far be-hind me.____

____ Where trou-bles melt like le-mon drops a - way a-bove the chim-ney tops, that's

where you'll find me. Some-where o - ver the rain-bow, blue-birds fly,

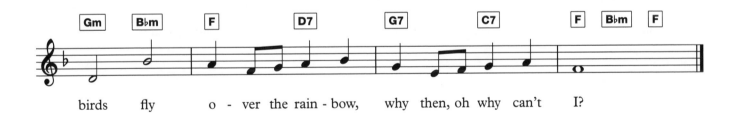

birds fly o - ver the rain - bow, why then, oh why can't I?

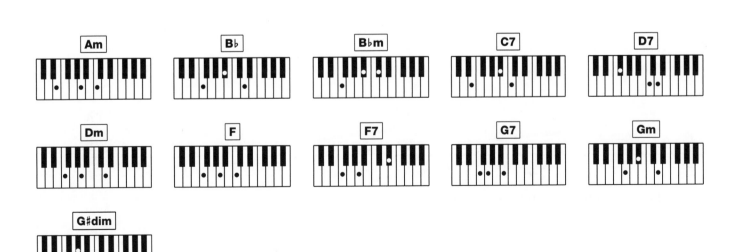

Smoke Gets In Your Eyes

Words by Otto Harbach / Music by Jerome Kern

Suggested Registration: Acoustic Guitar
Rhythm: Soft Rock
Tempo: ♩ = 72

They asked me how I knew my true love was true,_____

— I, of course, re - plied, 'Some-thing here in - side can - not be de -

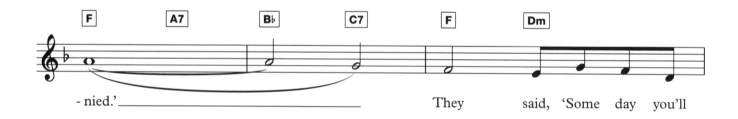

- nied.'_____ They said, 'Some day you'll

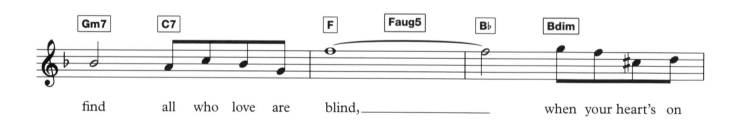

find all who love are blind,_____ when your heart's on

fire, you must re - a - lize, smoke gets in your eyes.'_____

So I chaffed them and I gai - ly laughed to think they could doubt my love.

Yet to - day,___ my love has flown a - way,___ I am with - out my love.

Now, laugh-ing friends de - ride tears I can-not hide,_____ so I smile and

say, 'When a love-ly flame dies, smoke gets in your eyes.'_____

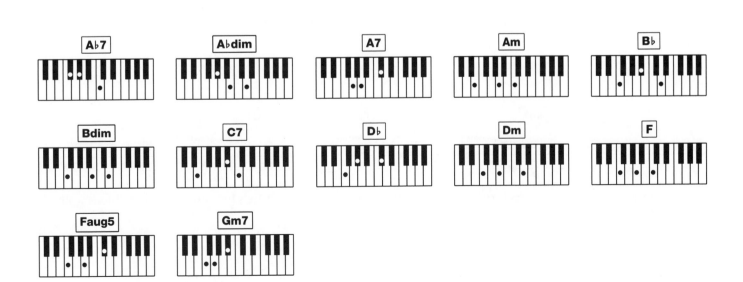

Stormy Weather

Words by Ted Koehler / Music by Harold Arlen

Suggested Registration: Vibraphone
Rhythm: Slow Swing
Tempo: ♩ = 78

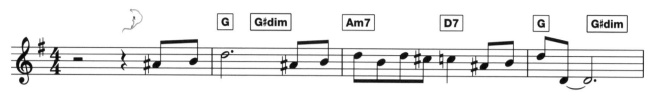

Don't know why   there's no   sun up in the sky, stor-my wea-ther,_

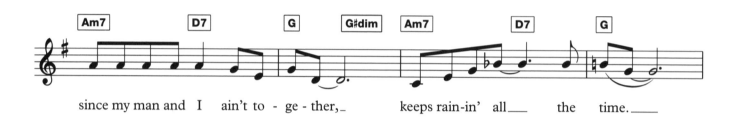

since my man and I   ain't to - ge - ther,_   keeps rain-in' all___   the   time.___

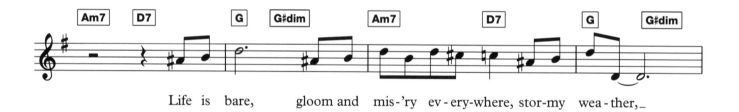

Life is   bare,   gloom and mis-'ry ev-ery-where, stor-my   wea-ther,_

just can't get my poor self to - ge - ther,_   I'm wea-ry all___   the   time,___   the

time,___   so wea-ry all___   the   time.___   When he went a - way the blues walked

in and met me,___ if he stays a - way, old rock - in' chair will get me.___

All I do is pray the Lord a - bove will let me___ walk in the sun once more. Can't go

on, ev - ery - thing I had is gone, stor - my wea - ther,_ since my man and I ain't to -

- ge - ther,___ keeps rain - in' all___ the time,_____

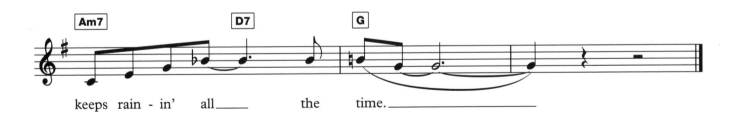

keeps rain - in' all___ the time._____

Summertime

By George Gershwin, Dubose Heyward, Dorothy Heyward and Ira Gershwin

Suggested Registration: Harmonica
Rhythm: Slow Swing
Tempo: ♩ = 74

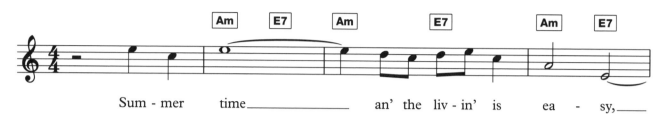

Sum - mer time_____ an' the liv - in' is ea - sy,_____

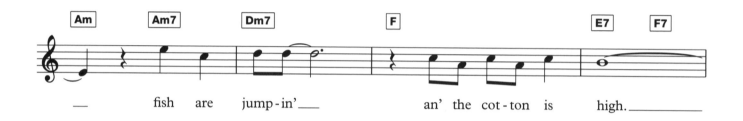

_____ fish are jump - in'___ an' the cot - ton is high._____

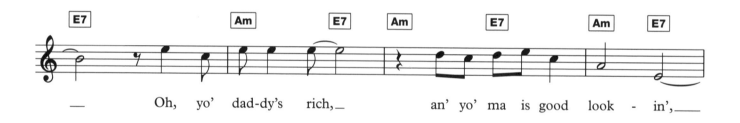

_____ Oh, yo' dad - dy's rich,_ an' yo' ma is good look - in',_____

_____ so hush lit - tle ba - by don'___ yo' cry._____

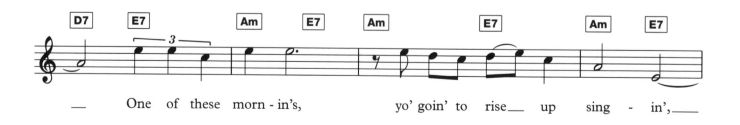

_____ One of these morn - in's, yo' goin' to rise___ up sing - in',_____

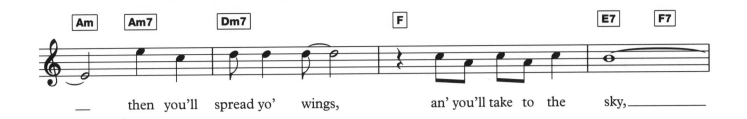

then you'll spread yo' wings, an' you'll take to the sky,_____

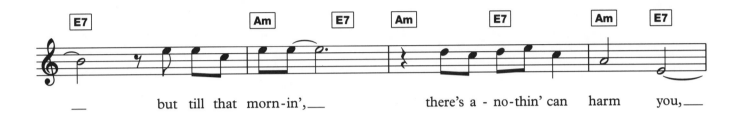

_____ but till that morn-in',___ there's a - no-thin' can harm you,___

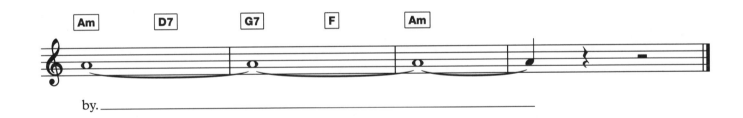

_____ with dad - dy and mom - my stand - in'

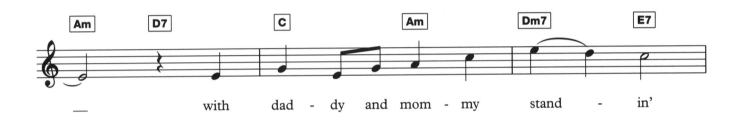

by._____

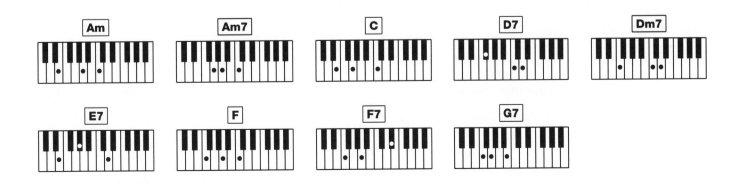

Walkin' My Baby Back Home

Words and Music by Roy Turk and Fred E Ahlert

Suggested Registration: Saxophone
Rhythm: Swing
Tempo: ♩ = 100

Classic Big B

Gee, it's great_ af - ter be - in' out late,_ walk-in' my ba - by back home,

arm in arm_ o - ver mea-dow and farm, walk-in' my ba - by back home.

We go 'long_ har-mon-iz-in' a song, or I'm re - cit - ing a poem,

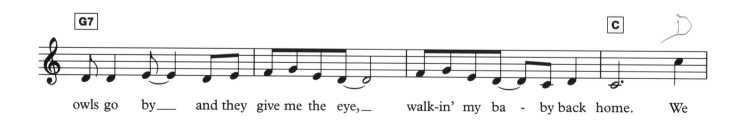

owls go by__ and they give me the eye,_ walk-in' my ba - by back home. We

stop for a while, she gives me a smile, and snug-gles her head to my chest. We

start in to pet,_ and that's when I get_ her pow - der all o - ver my vest._

Af - ter I___ kind - a straight-en my tie,_ she has to bor - row my comb,

one kiss then, I con - tin - ue a - gain,_ walk-in' my ba - by back home.

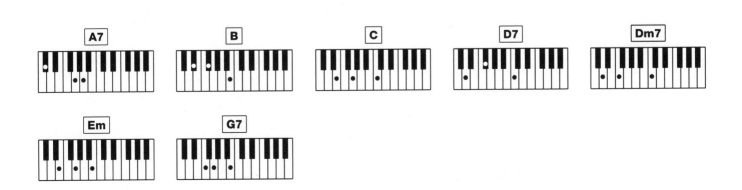

The Way You Look Tonight

Words by Dorothy Fields / Music by Jerome Kern

Suggested Registration: Strings
Rhythm: Soft Rock
Tempo: ♩ = 72

Some day,   when I'm aw-f'ly low,   when the world is cold,

I will feel a glow just think-ing   of   you,   and the way you look   to - night.

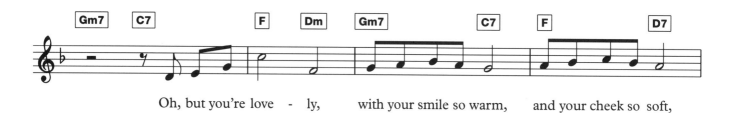

Oh, but you're love - ly,   with your smile so warm,   and your cheek so soft,

there is no-thing for me but to love   you,   just the way you look   to - night.

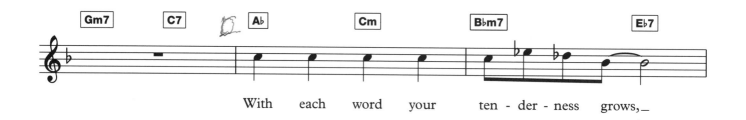

With   each   word   your   ten - der - ness   grows,__

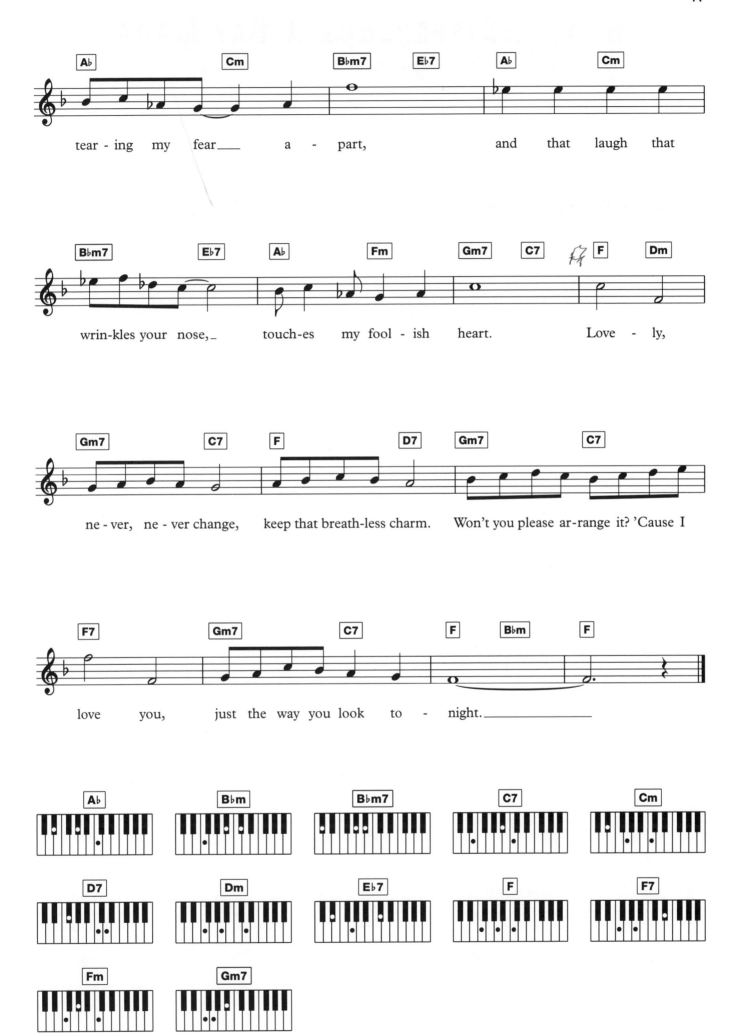

What A Difference A Day Made

Music and Spanish Words by Maria Grever / English Words by Stanley Adams

Suggested Registration: Acoustic Guitar
Rhythm: Rhumba / Latin
Tempo: ♩ = 124

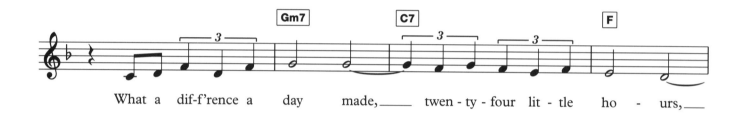

What a dif-f'rence a day made,_____ twen-ty-four lit-tle ho - urs,_____

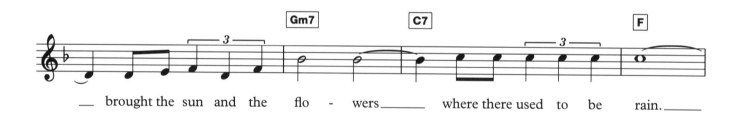

_ brought the sun and the flo - wers_____ where there used to be rain._____

_ My yes-ter-day was blue, dear,_____ to-day, I'm part of you dear,_

_ my lone-ly nights are through, dear,_____ since you said you were mine._____

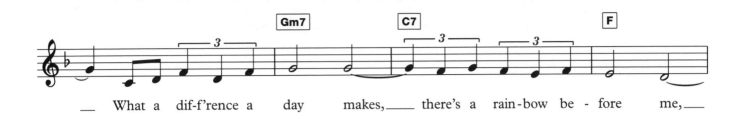

What a dif-f'rence a day makes,___ there's a rain-bow be - fore me,___

___ skies a-bove can't be stor - my,___ since that mo-ment of bliss, that thrill-ing

kiss, it's hea-ven when you___ find ro-mance on your me - nu.___

___ What a dif-f'rence a day made, and the dif-f'rence is you.___

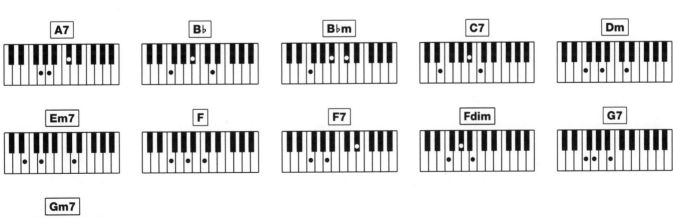

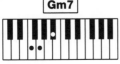

When Your Old Wedding Ring Was New

Words by Charles McCarthy and Joe Solieri / Music by Bert Douglas

Suggested Registration: Clarinet
Rhythm: Swing
Tempo: ♩ = 120

When your old wed-ding ring was new. _____

— and each dream that we dreamed came true, _____

— I re-mem-ber with pride ____ how we stood side by side, _

— what a beau-ti-ful pic-ture you made as my

bride. Ev - en though sil - ver crowns your hair,_____

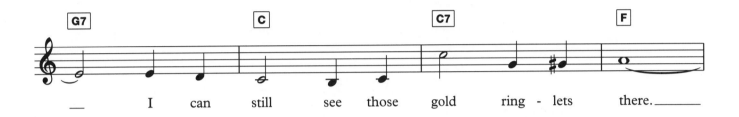

__ I can still see those gold ring - lets there._____

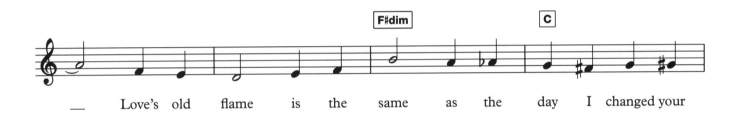

__ Love's old flame is the same as the day I changed your

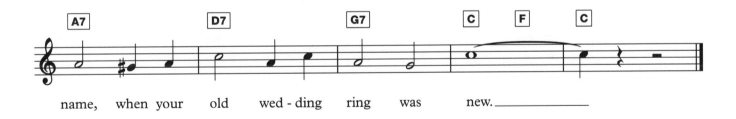

name, when your old wed - ding ring was new._____

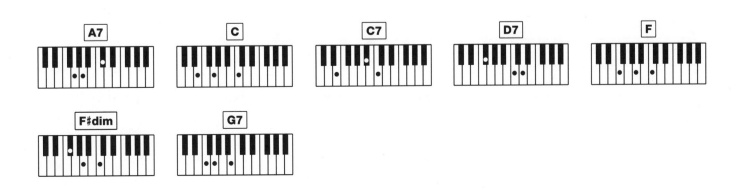

You Go To My Head

Words by Haven Gillespie / Music by J Fred Coots

Suggested Registration: Strings
Rhythm: Slow Swing
Tempo: ♩ = 90

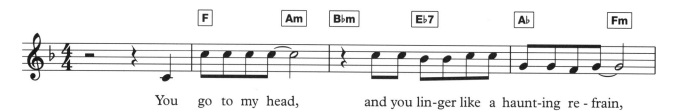

You go to my head, and you lin-ger like a haunt-ing re - frain,

and I find you spin-ning round in my brain, like the bub-bles in a glass of cham-pagne. __

__ You go to my head, like a sip of spark-ling Bur-gun-dy Brew,

and I find the ve - ry men-tion of you, _ like the kick-er in a ju-lep or two. ___

__ The thrill of the thought that you might give a thought to my plea casts a spell o-ver me.

__ Still I say to my-self, 'Get a hold of your-self, can't you see that it ne - ver can

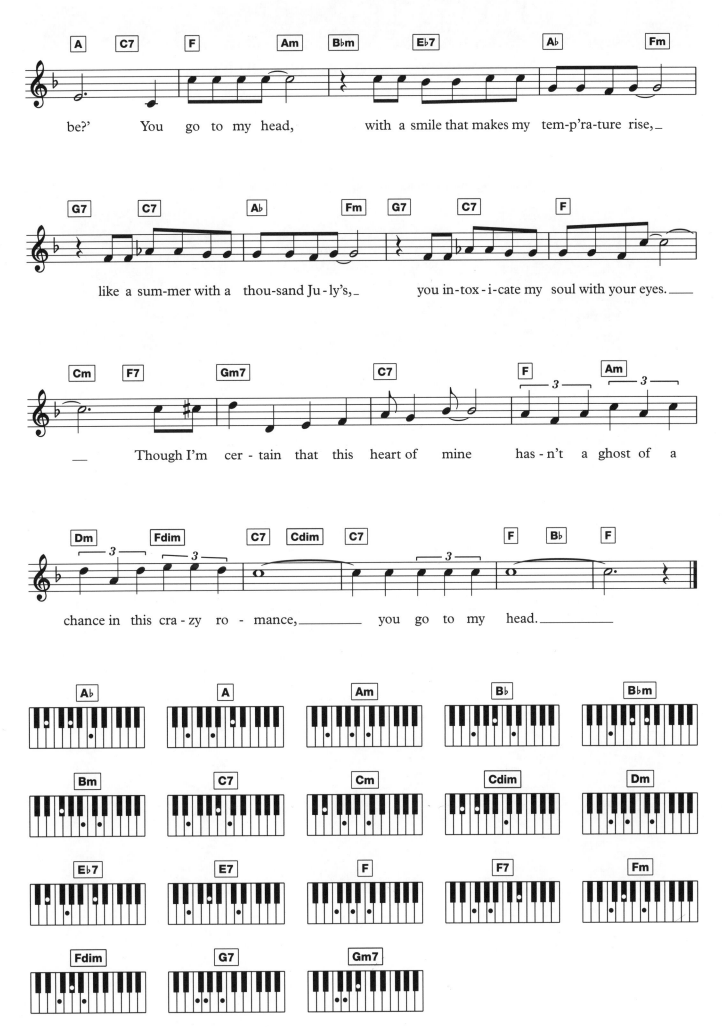

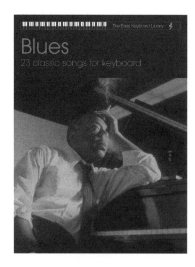
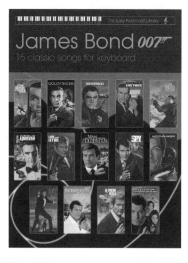

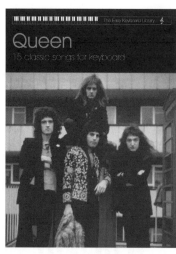